ZONE 13

D1579508

Space
Weed

DAVID ORME

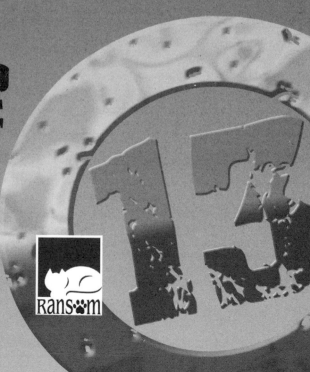

Ransom

Space Weed
by David Orme
Illustrated by Jorge Mongiovi and Ulises Carpintero
Cover photograph: © Pauline S Mills

Published by Ransom Publishing Ltd.
Radley House, 8 St. Cross Road, Winchester, Hampshire, SO23 9HX, UK
www.ransom.co.uk

ISBN   978 184167 466 7

First published in 2011

Copyright © 2011 Ransom Publishing Ltd.

Illustrations copyright © 2011 Jorge Mongiovi and Ulises Carpintero

Printed in India by Imprint Digital Ltd.
Originally published in 1998 by Stanley Thornes Publishers Ltd.

A CIP catalogue record of this book is available from the British Library.

The rights of David Orme to be identified as the author and of Jorge Mongiovi
and Ulises Carpintero to be identified as the illustrators of this Work have been
asserted by them in accordance with sections 77 and 78 of the Copyright, Design
and Patents Act 1988.

CONTENTS

NOT FOR THE PUBLIC TO KNOW
TOP SECRET
ZONE 13 FILES ONLY

NOT FOR THE PUBLIC TO KNOW
TOP SECRET
ZONE 13 FILES ONLY

THE ASTEROID

The asteroid had travelled round the Sun for millions of years. Nothing had changed on its frozen surface – until now!

A second asteroid was on a collision course. Nearer and nearer it came. With enormous force, the two asteroids smashed together. One of them was broken into millions of tiny pieces of rock and ice. These pieces spread out into space in all directions. Some started to orbit the Sun. Some hit Mars, and Jupiter. And some reached the Earth ...

THE PLANTS BEGIN TO GROW

The shower of shooting stars was seen all over the Earth. Most people didn't notice them. They didn't have time to stand and look at the sky. People who did see them soon forgot about it. Astronomers were excited for a short time. Then they forgot about it, too.

'Meteorites are always hitting the Earth. There's nothing special about them,' the astronomers said.

Some of the meteorites were burnt up completely before they reached the ground. Some came down in the sea. Some buried themselves in the Earth.

As these meteorites cooled, something strange started happening.

Cracks appeared on them. Tiny white shoots started to come from the cracks. The shoots buried themselves in the ground. Roots started to grow. When the roots found water, yellow shoots appeared and grew upwards towards the light.

Altogether, there were only about a hundred plants in the whole world, but they seemed to be able to grow anywhere. In deserts, on mountain tops and in muddy swamps, the plants grew, tall and strong.

At first, no one noticed them. They were just plants – and what harm can a plant do?

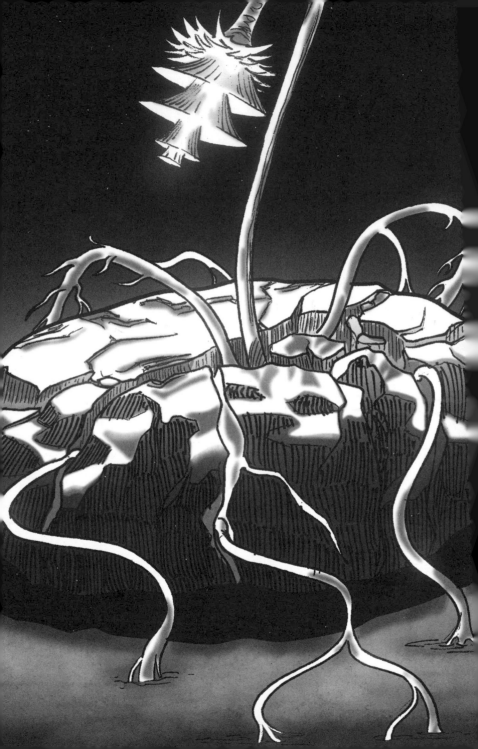

BLOODSUCKERS

Old Joe Tyler had a small farm in West Virginia, U.S.A. He had no family. Sometimes, he didn't see anyone for days. He didn't mind. He liked it that way.

Joe was checking out one of his fields. He wanted to use it for some young horses. He wanted to check how well the grass was growing before he put the horses in.

The grass looked good. Joe was pleased. Then he saw something yellow near the far fence. He drove his tractor over.

It was a plant. Joe had never seen one like it before. It was tall, with drooping yellow leaves. On the very top of the plant there was a huge yellow flower.

He jumped down from the tractor to have a closer look.

As he got near, the plant seemed to bend towards him. A cloud of yellow dust shot into Joe's face. He felt dizzy and started to fall.

Soon he was lying on the ground. He could see and hear, and feel the ground underneath him.

But he couldn't move a muscle ...

ooo//ooo

Will and Simon were brothers. They both
loved walking in the hills and mountains of
Wales.

They were heading down a mountain path
when Will saw something unusual.

'What's that plant?'

Simon looked at it.

'That looks pretty weird! Let's get a bit closer.'

'They climbed over rocks to reach the plant. Will got there first. Simon saw the plant bend over. A puff of something yellow came from the plant. He saw his brother fall down and lie still on the ground.

Simon rushed over to try and help his brother.

Before he could get to Will, he breathed in some of the yellow dust. He felt dizzy. Soon he was on the ground as well.

Simon watched his brother in alarm. Something very odd was happening around the place where Will lay. White roots were coming up all around him. Soon they started to grow over him like a white net.

Gradually the roots changed colour, from white to dark red. The roots were growing into Will's body! The plant was drinking his blood!

Simon tried to scream, but he couldn't make a sound.

He tried to imagine what it was like for Will. The roots were digging into his body, sucking out every drop of blood.

Will couldn't move a muscle – but he could still feel everything!

THE SEEDS

By the time Joe's body was found, there wasn't much left to see. All the liquid in his body had been sucked out. There was nothing left but dry skin and bone.

ooo//ooo

Simon had been lucky. He was too far away from the plant for the roots to reach him. After an hour, he had been able to move again. He had rushed down the mountainside to get help. It was too late for Will.

ooo//ooo

Soon, reports of the terrible plants came in from all around the world. Scientists held meetings over the Internet. They wondered where the plants were coming from, and how many there were. One scientist thought that they might have come from space in meteorites. Other scientists just laughed at that. They thought it was a crazy idea.

They all agreed on one thing. The plants had to be destroyed. They must be burnt to ashes!

Only one other plant had been discovered in Britain. Dr Jack Meredith was in charge of destroying it. He and his assistants set off with their equipment. They wore special clothing to keep out the yellow dust.

'It must be the plant's pollen,' Jack had said. 'I guess it contains a powerful nerve poison.'

The plant was growing high up on a hillside. When Jack and his team reached it, they took photos and videos of it. Then one of the team aimed a flame thrower.

The plant burst into flames. Then something unexpected happened. The top of the plant burst open. Thousands of tiny seeds flew out. Each one had a tiny parachute.

The team watched in horror as the seeds sailed away in the wind.

'Fire helps the plants to release their seeds!' groaned Jack. 'We've made the problem worse!'

NOT FOR THE PUBLIC TO KNOW
TOP SECRET
ZONE 13 FILES ONLY

5

THE SEEDS ESCAPE

A new message went out. 'Don't burn the plants!' But many of them had been burnt already. Thousands of seeds had blown far and wide, all around the world.

The seeds were worse than the plants. If they landed on a person or animal, they started sending a root down into the skin. People tried to pull the seeds away from them, but even a tiny piece of root would grow and spread through the body. When the person or

animal died, flower shoots would break through the skin. This seemed to be a plant that just couldn't be beaten!

ooo//ooo

Jack was put in charge of finding ways to destroy the plant. He had a laboratory, and rows of greenhouses. In the greenhouses he

grew the plants and experimented on them.
He worked with another scientist – Sally
Lewis. Sally was a brilliant scientist and an
expert on plants.

The scientists had tried all sorts of ways to
kill the plants. Ordinary weedkiller was
useless. The plants seemed to grow stronger
when they were sprayed. Chopping them

down before the flowers came didn't help. The roots went down deep, and more shoots were growing by the next day.

In one of the greenhouses a plant was fully grown. Any day now its seed pod would burst. The greenhouse was specially sealed to stop the seeds escaping. No one was allowed in without special clothes.

One morning the scientist found that a rat had managed to get in during the night. The white roots were growing all over it, drinking the last of its blood.

ooo//ooo

Sally and Jack were working late one night. They knew the world had a big problem. The seeds from the first plants were growing everywhere. Once the plants let their seeds go

no one was safe out of doors without special clothes.

It was a windy night. The big oak trees outside the laboratory were bending in the wind. Sally looked out.

'That's the trouble with those seeds,' she said. 'They can blow anywhere in the wind.'

Just then there was a cracking sound, then an enormous crash. Jack rushed to the door and looked out. He came back seconds later.

'Quick! Put your special clothes on! A branch has fallen on the greenhouse! The seeds are escaping!'

NOT FOR THE PUBLIC

TOP SECRET

ZONE 13 FILES ONLY

32

6

DEATH ON THE M25

The big branch had hit one of the plants growing in the greenhouse. The seed pod had burst open. The seeds were blowing everywhere in the strong wind.

The M25 motorway was a mile from the laboratory. Most people had their car windows shut, because of the wind. A tiny crack was enough for the seeds to get in. Soon, cars and trucks were going out of control. People were

screaming as the tiny roots started to grow into their hands and faces.

Police and firefighters were soon on the scene, but they were attacked by the seeds too. Fire started in some of the piled-up cars and trucks. No one could get to the people trapped inside. It was too dangerous to walk around in the open.

Even when people managed to escape from the flames, the seeds were waiting for them. Hundreds of people suffered a horrible death that night.

Jack and Sally were blamed for the disaster. They shouldn't have been growing the plants so near to the motorway, people said. The greenhouse wasn't safe. They hadn't managed to find a way to kill the plants anyway. All they had done was make it worse.

Jack and Sally were out of a job. And all around the world, the plants carried on growing.

COMMON GREENFLY

Jack was sitting in his garden, reading the papers. Reports of deaths were coming from all over the world. Some people had been sprayed with pollen, then sucked dry while they lay helpless on the ground. Others had been the victims of the seeds.

Next door, his neighbour Mr Parry was busy working. Jack went over to talk to him.

'I've never seen your roses look better, Mr Parry.'

'That's because the greenfly aren't attacking them this year,' said the old gardener.

Jack was surprised at this. Greenfly were always a problem.

'Why do you think that is?'

'That's easy!' said Mr Parry. 'You don't eat bread and water when you can get steak, do you? The greenfly have found something tastier to eat!'

He pointed to the corner of his garden. One of the yellow plants was growing there.

'Mr Parry! That's a very dangerous plant!'

'It doesn't look dangerous to me. And it helps my roses!'

Jack looked closely. The yellow plant was covered in greenfly. They were sucking the juice out of the leaves. It was nearly dead already!

Jack rushed indoors to the telephone. Maybe the problem was solved!

Later that day, Jack rang Sally at her home. It had been a bad day for Jack.

'No one in the government will listen!' he said. 'They say that I only make things worse!'

'Forget the government,' said Sally. 'Tell the world! Put what you have found on the Internet!'

Within minutes, the message was flashing around the world. 'Common greenfly will kill the plants. If you do not have them in your country, send for them. Release them near the plants. They will do the rest.'

Britain had plenty of greenfly. The strange plants were being sucked to death.

The government was delighted. Jack's mistakes were soon forgiven.

NOT FOR THE PUBLIC TO KNOW
TOP SECRET
ZONE 13 FILES ONLY

UNCOMMON GREENFLY

One morning a few weeks later, Jack was sitting in his garden again. Mr Parry did not seem to be such a happy man today.

'Look at my garden! Ruined!'

The roses were all dead. Jack looked closely at them. Greenfly! But he had never seen greenfly that big before!

They were huge, at least five times as big as normal. They were moving off the dead roses, looking for something else to eat.

Jack guessed what had happened.

The greenfly had drunk the juices of the plants. The plant was full of strange chemicals. The greenfly had changed. They would breed, and maybe destroy all plant life on Earth!

He hadn't been able to kill the plants with poison. He guessed that the greenfly couldn't be killed that way either.

He had told the world to release greenfly. It was his fault – again!

He didn't think things could get much worse.

There were no living plants left in the gardens. They had all been sucked dry by the greenfly.

It was then that he felt a sharp pain on his hand. Then another one on his face.

They greenfly had eaten all the plants. Now they were looking for blood.

And they just kept coming.

NOT FOR THE PUBLIC TO KNOW
TOP SECRET
ZONE 13 FILES ONLY

ABOUT THE AUTHOR

David Orme is an expert on strange, unexplained events. For his protection (and yours) we cannot show a photograph of him.

David created the Zone 13 files to record the cases he studied. Some of these files really do involve aliens, but many do not. Aliens are not everywhere. Just in most places.

These stories are all taken from the Zone 13 files. They will not be here for long. Read them while you can.

But don't close your eyes when you go to sleep at night. **They** will be watching you.